Odd Sti

No Intelligent Life Here

TONY LOPES

ℛℛ
RAVETTE PUBLISHING

Printed and bound in Malta for
Ravette Publishing Limited
Unit 3, Tristar Centre
Star Road, Partridge Green
West Sussex RH13 8RA

ISBN: 1 84161 224 3

to Lori, my soul mate

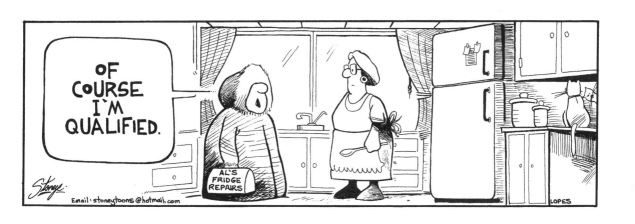
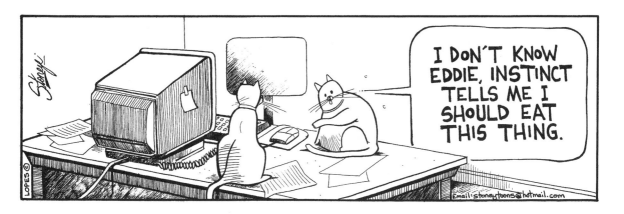

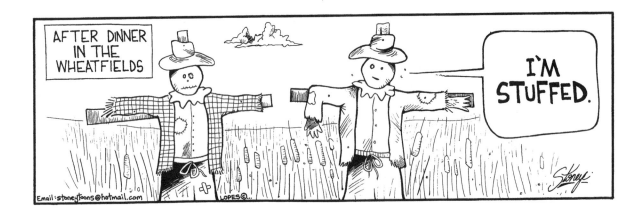

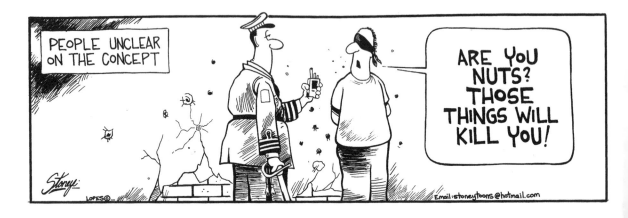

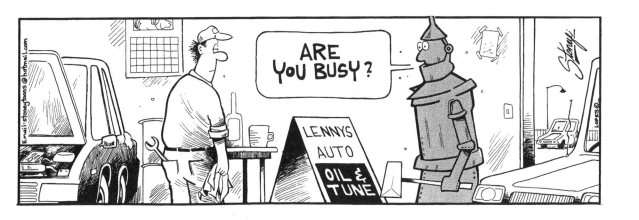

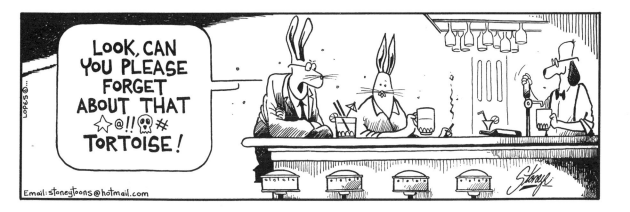

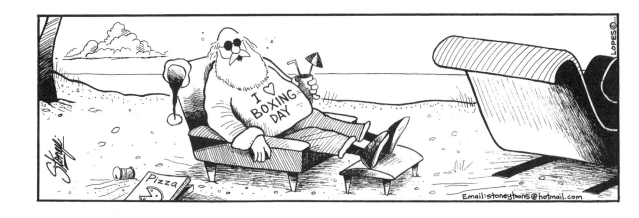
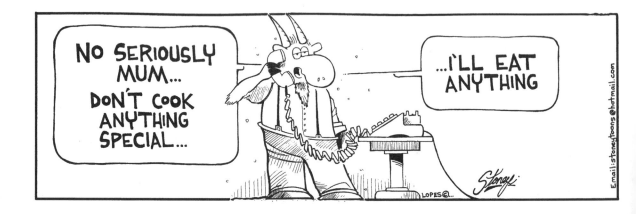

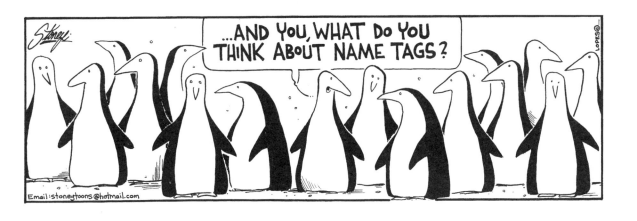

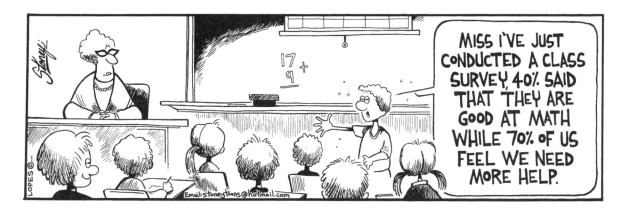

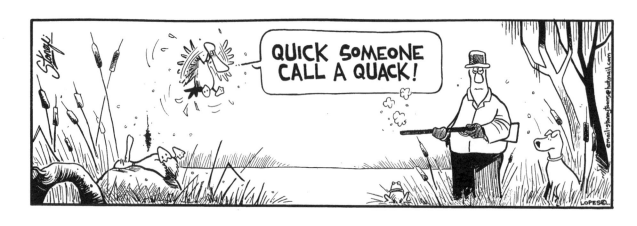

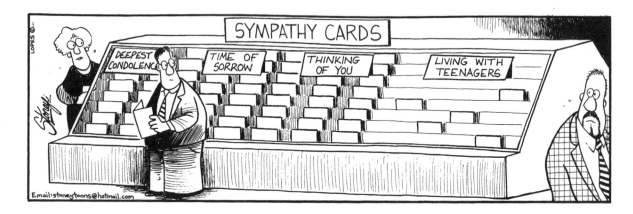

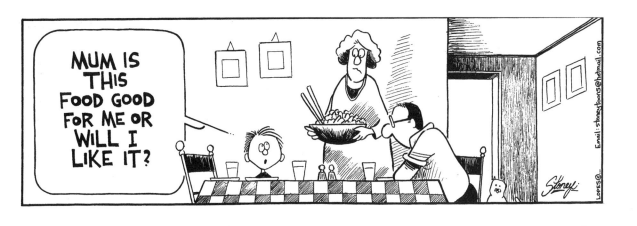

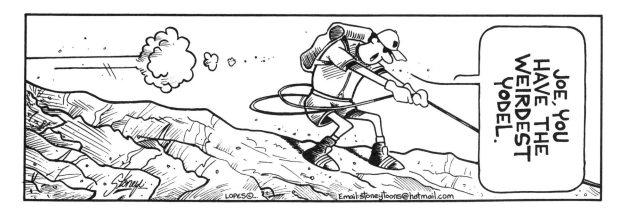

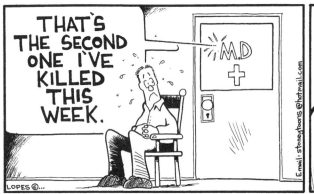
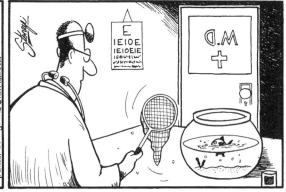
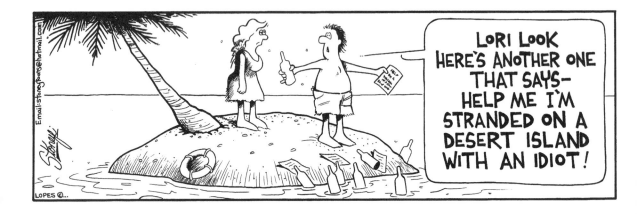

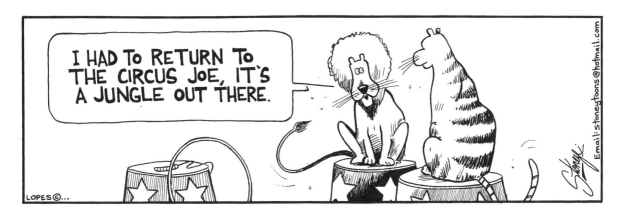

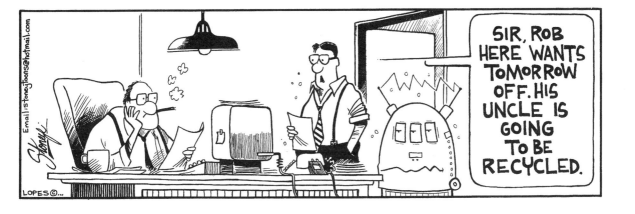

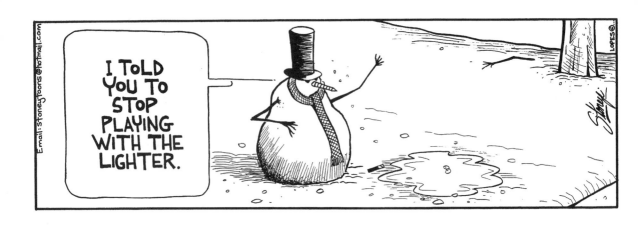

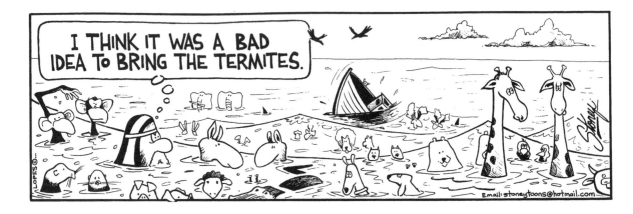

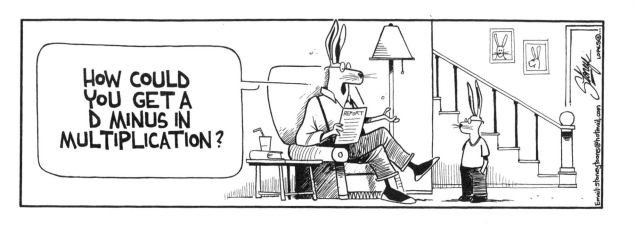
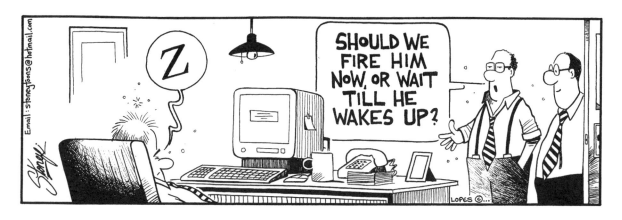

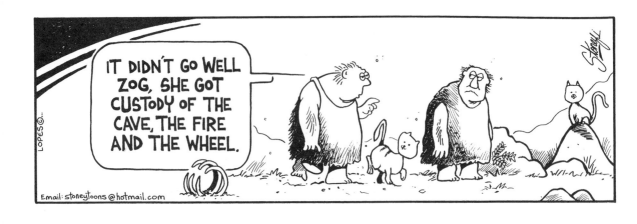

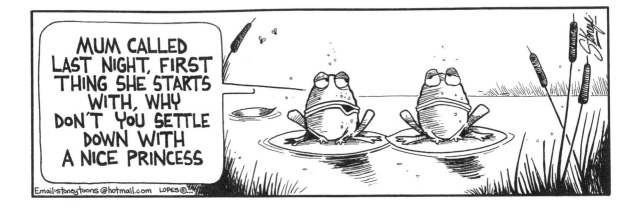

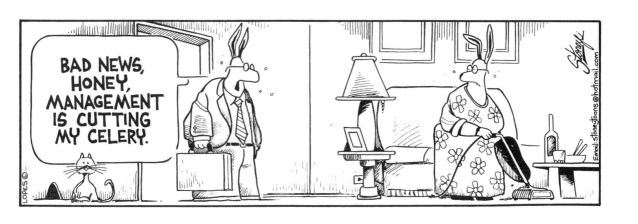

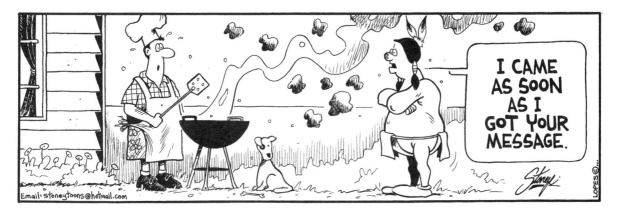

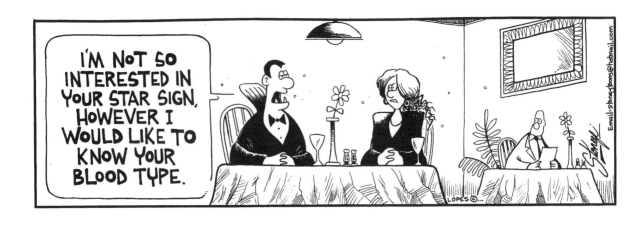

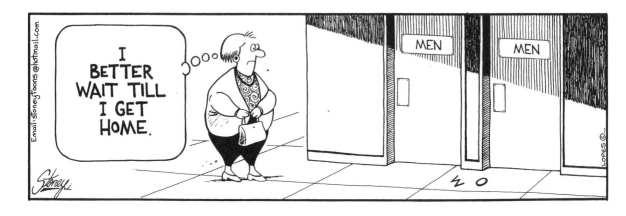

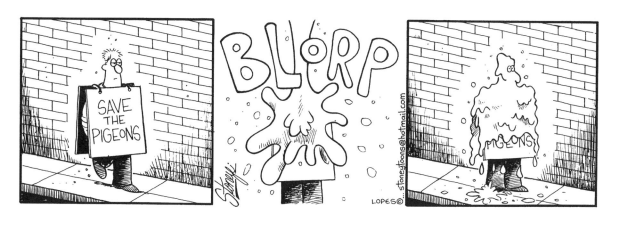

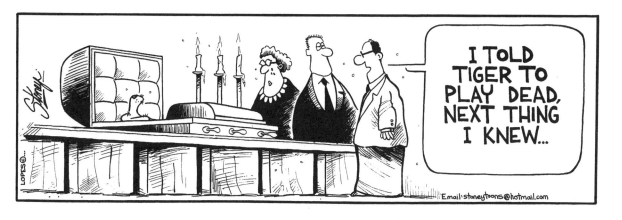

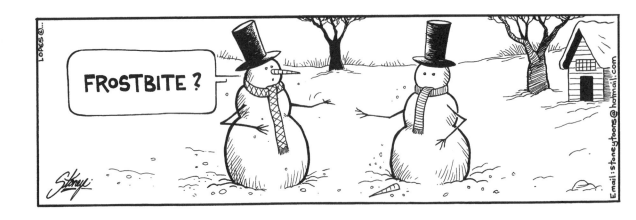

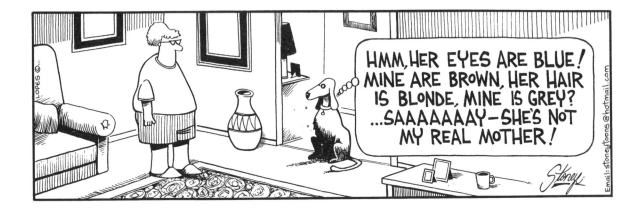

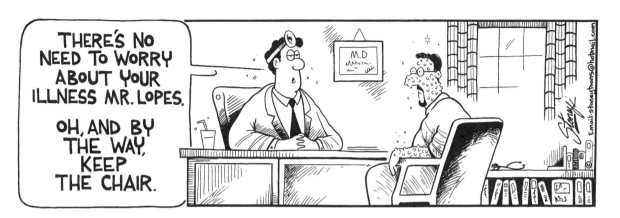

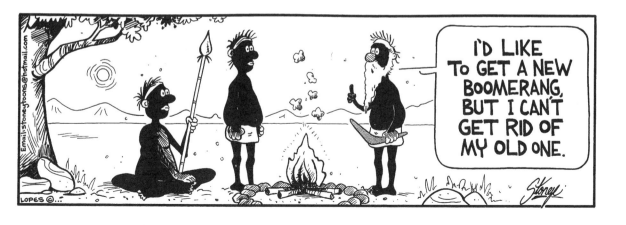

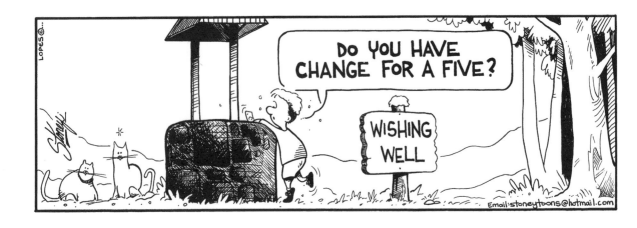
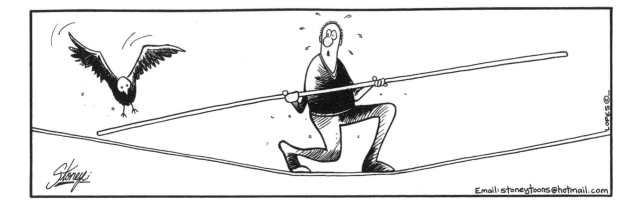

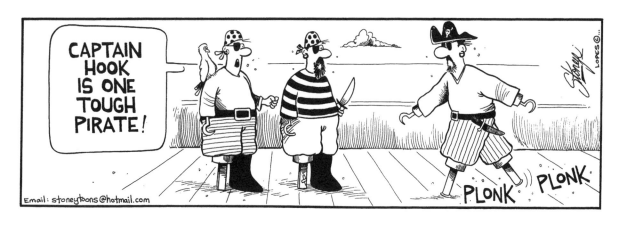

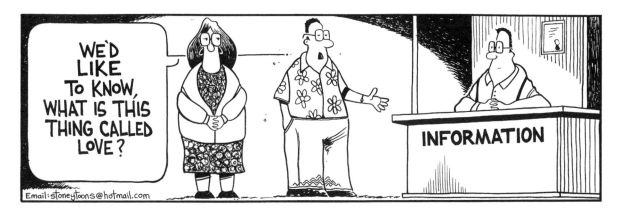

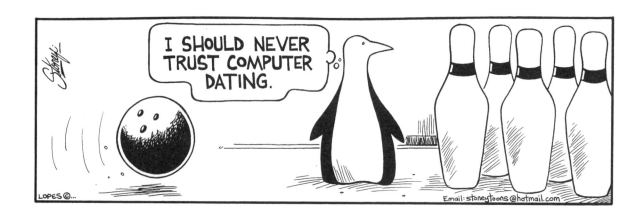

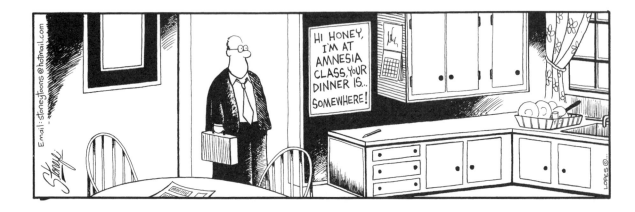

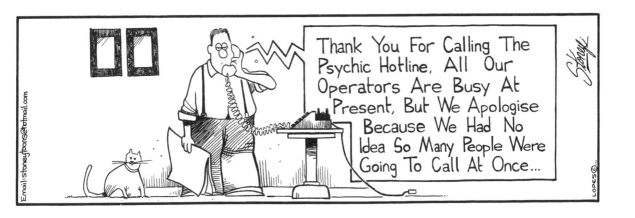

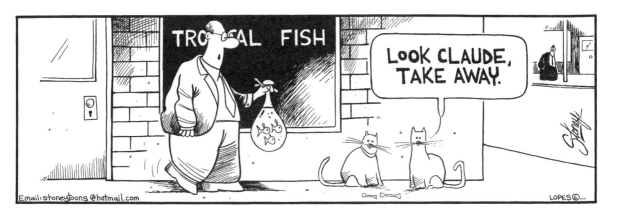

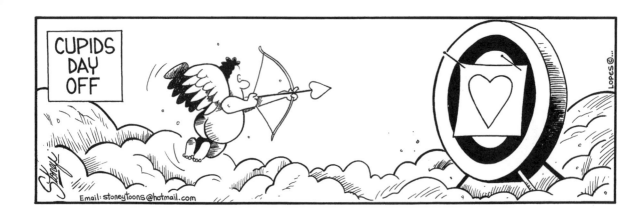

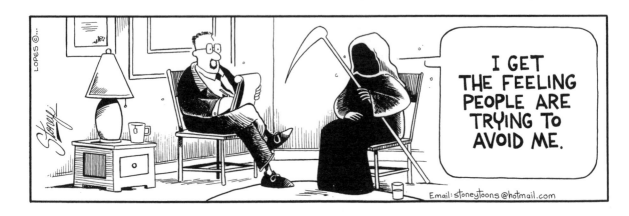

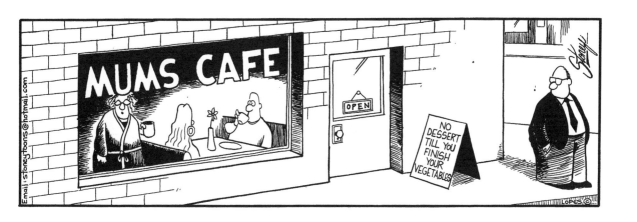

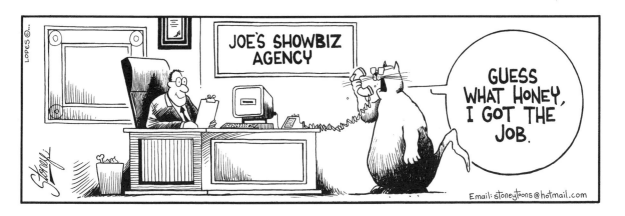

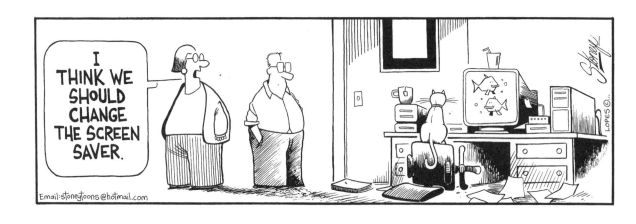

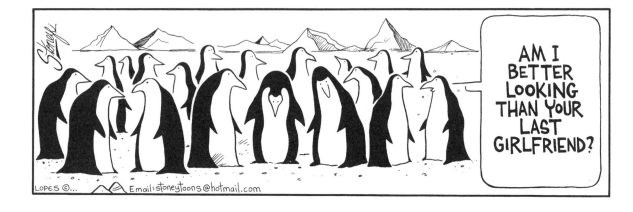

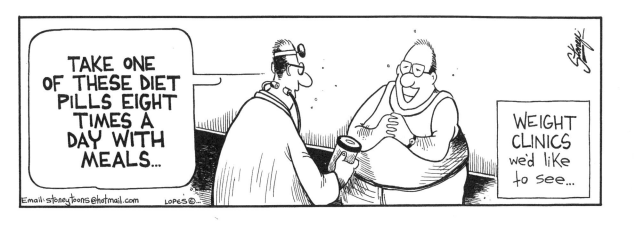

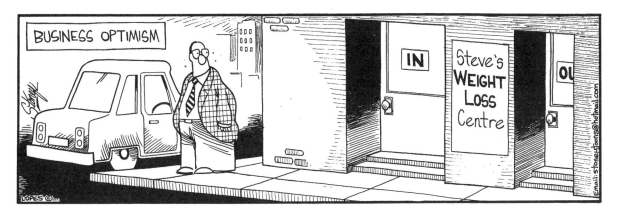

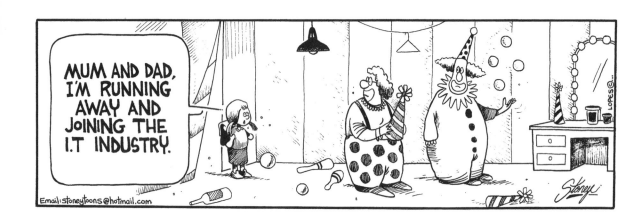
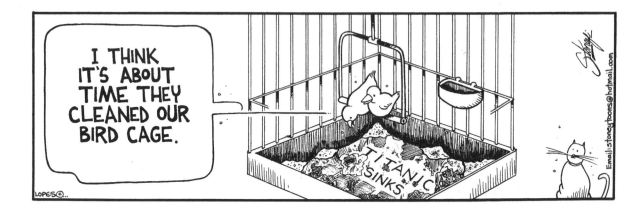

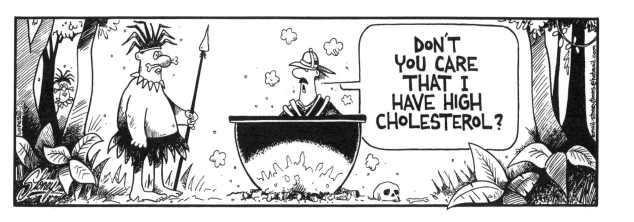

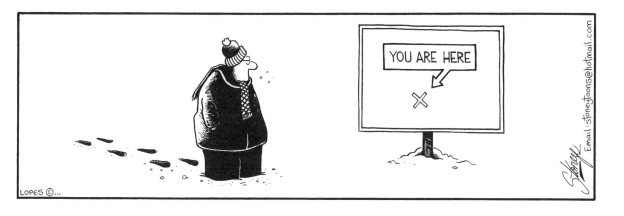

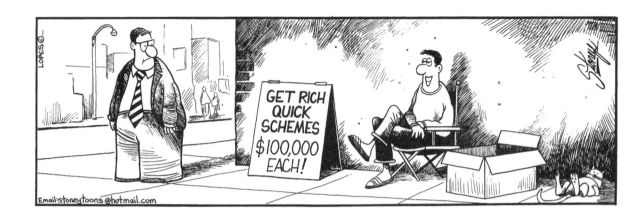

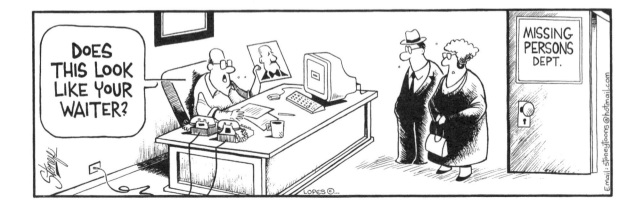

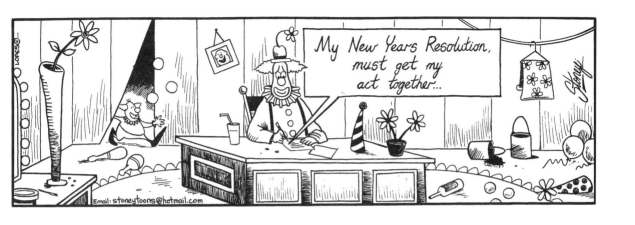

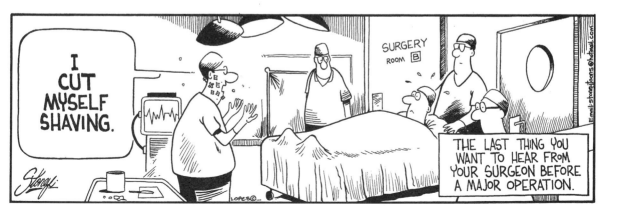

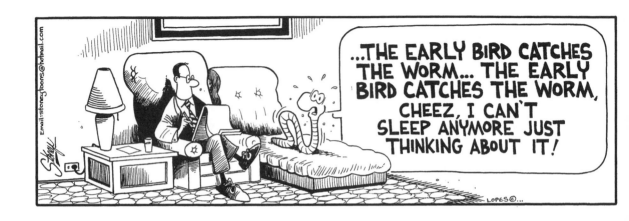

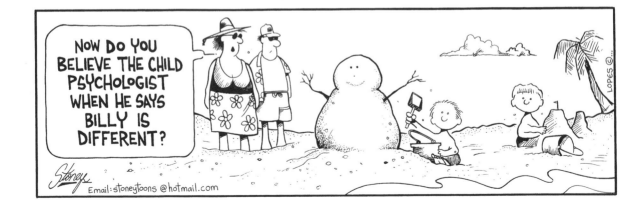

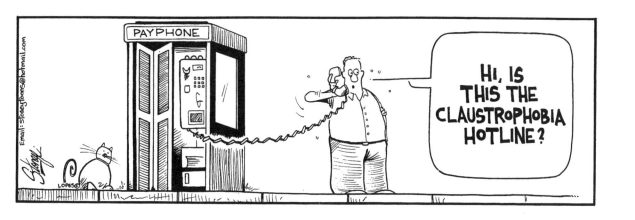

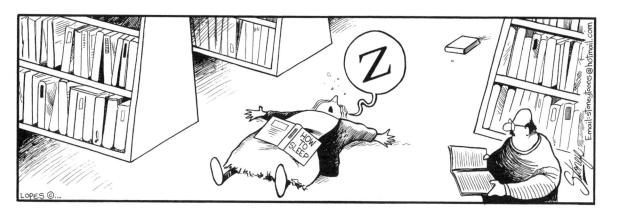

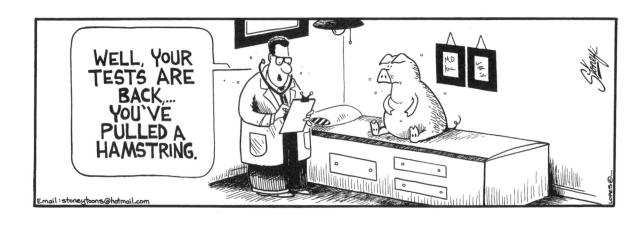

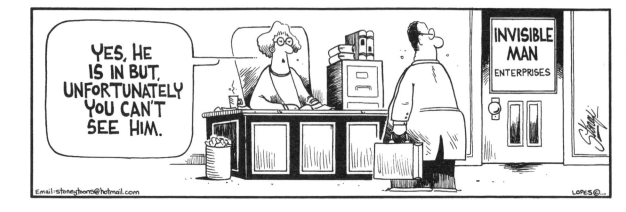

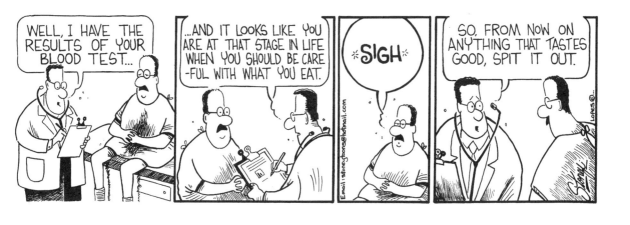

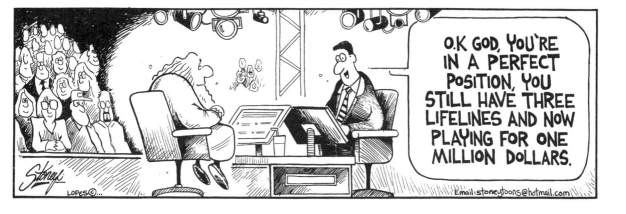

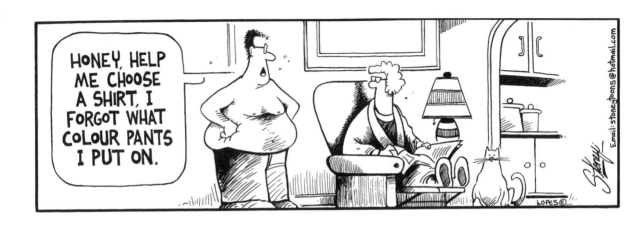
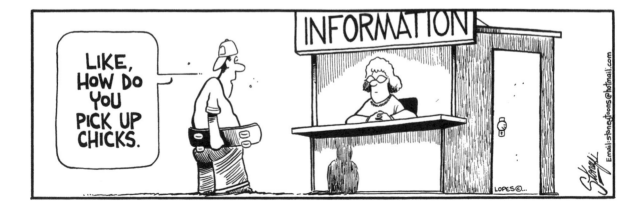

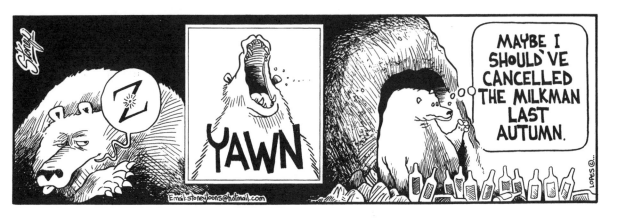

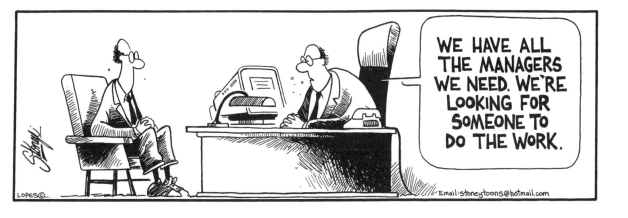

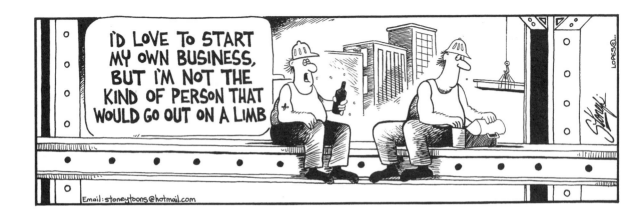

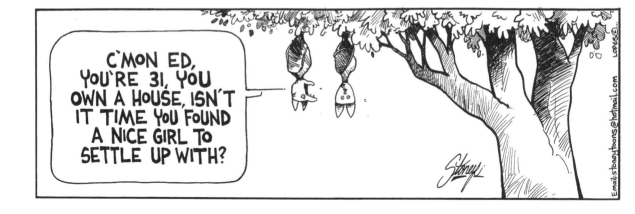

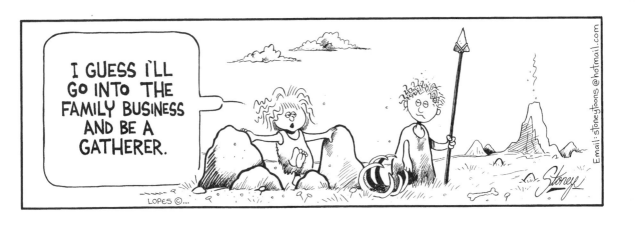

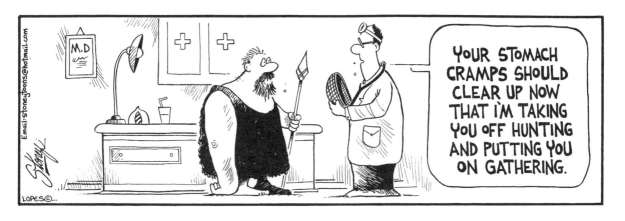

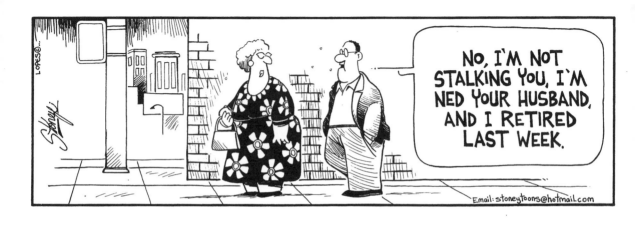
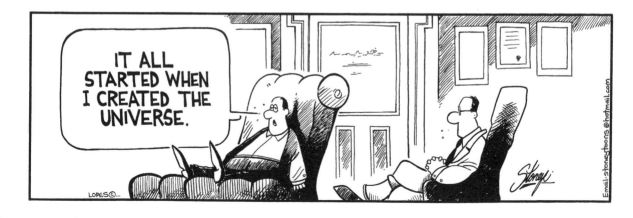

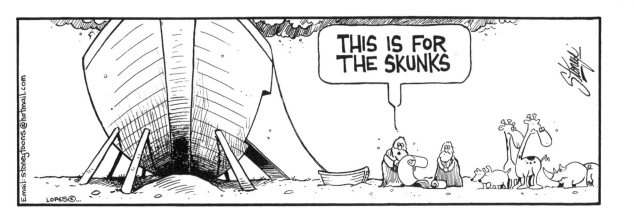

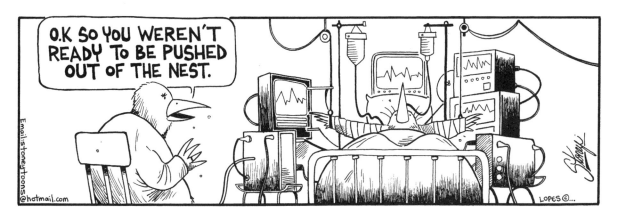

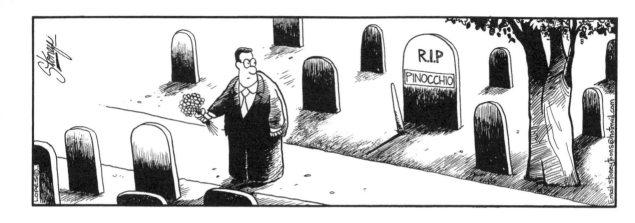
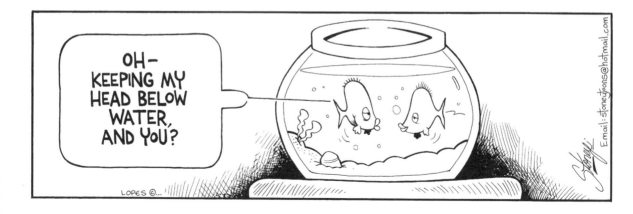

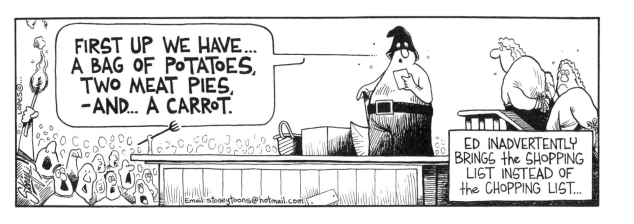

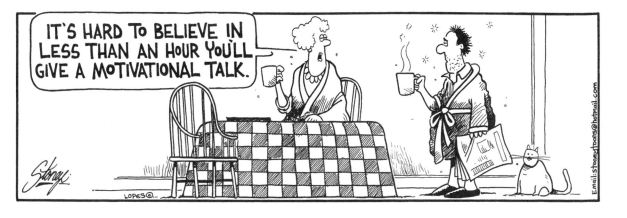

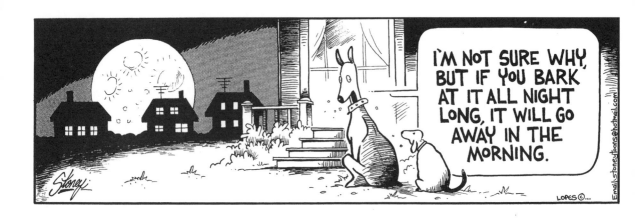

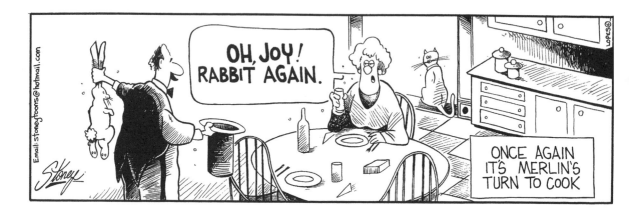

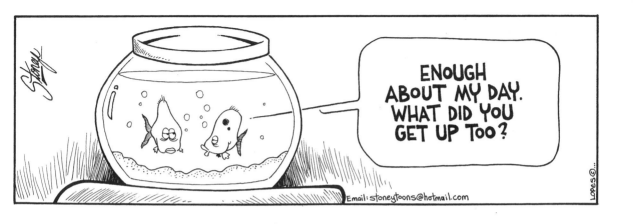

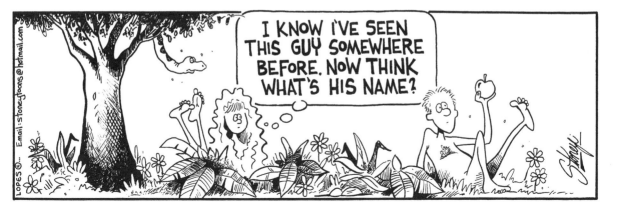

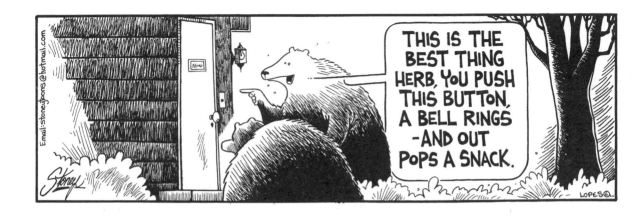
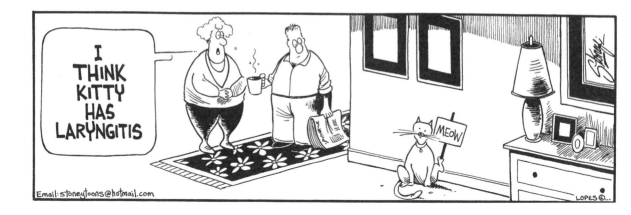

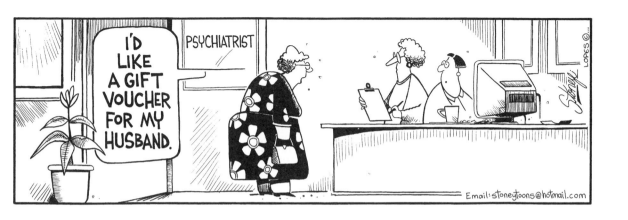

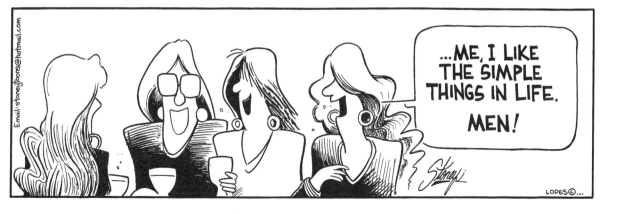

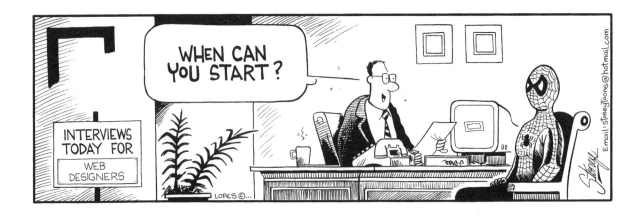

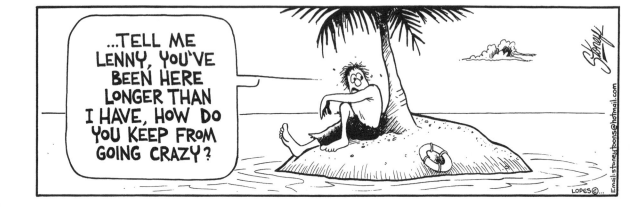

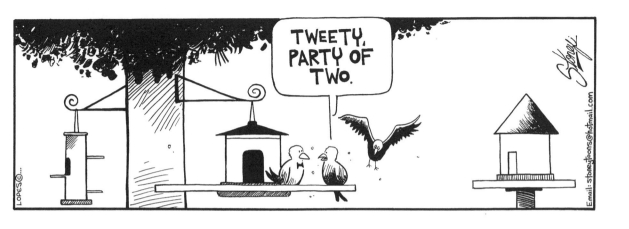

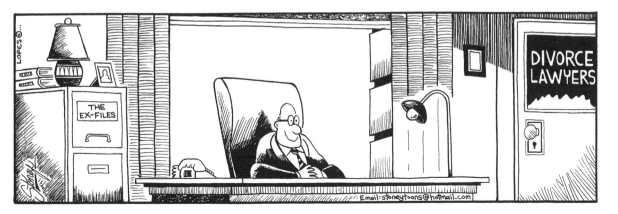

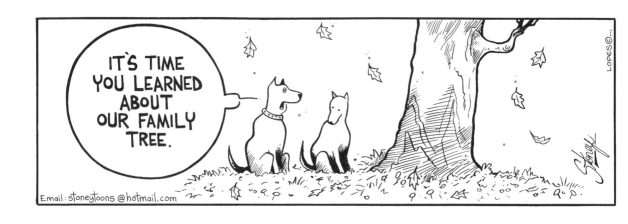
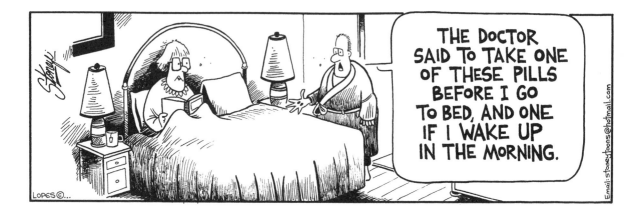

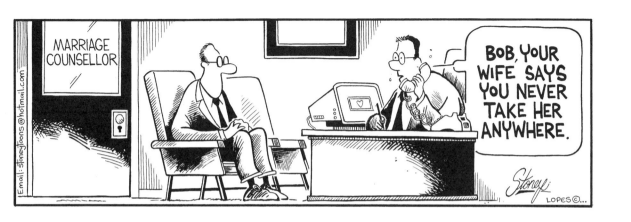
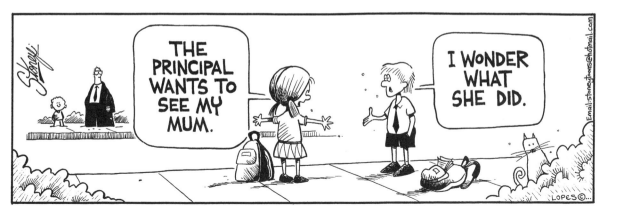

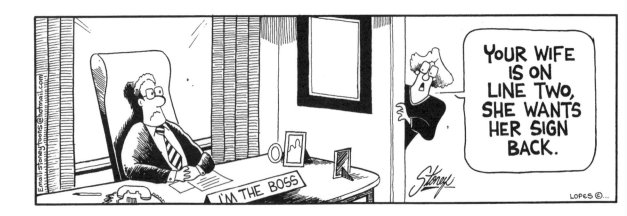

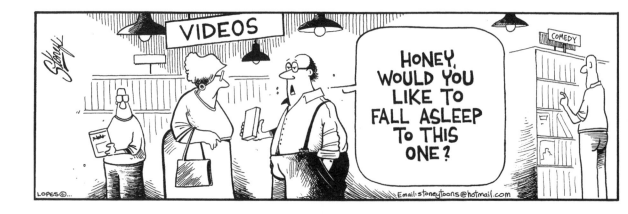

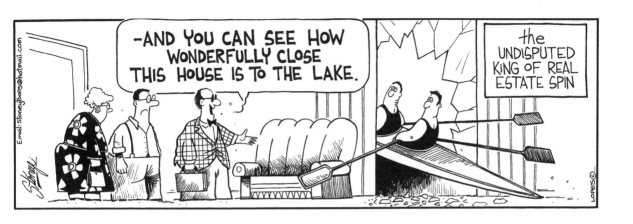

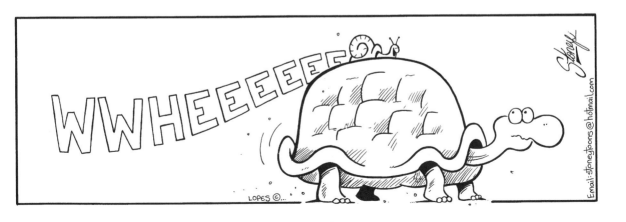

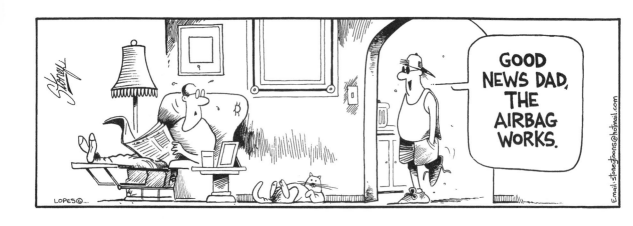

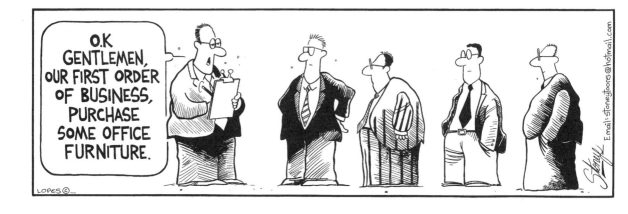

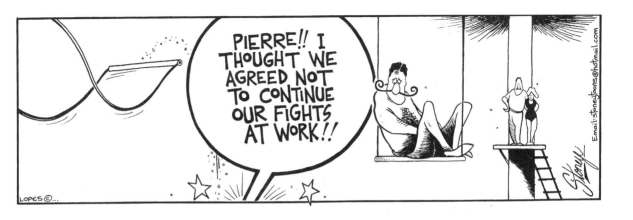

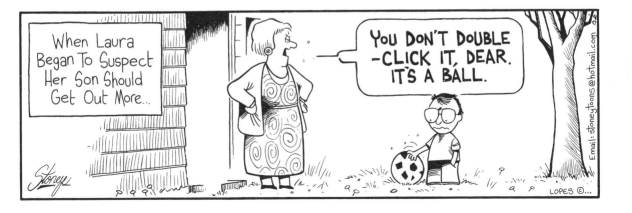

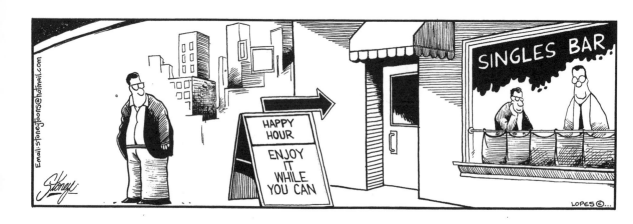

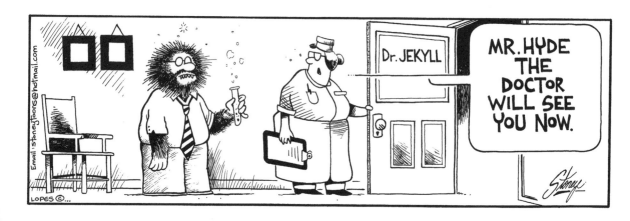

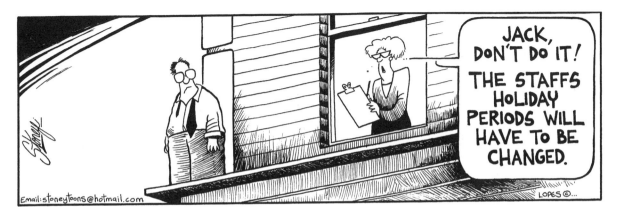

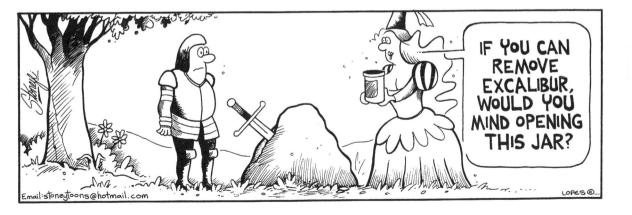

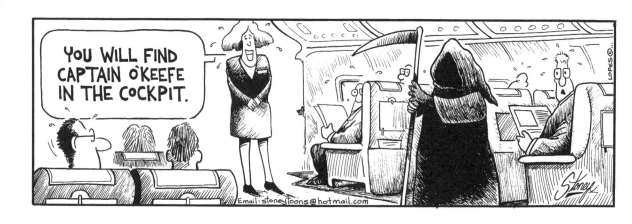

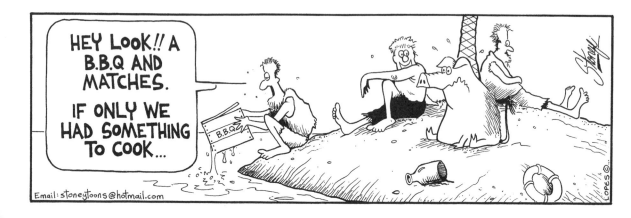

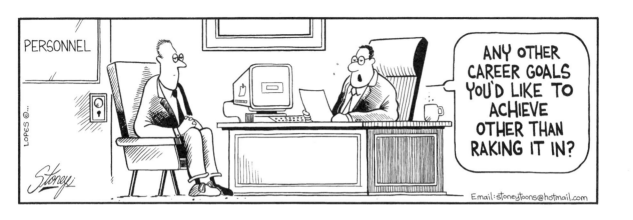
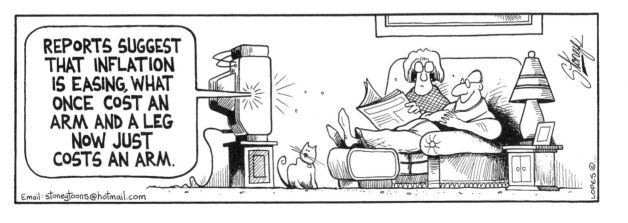

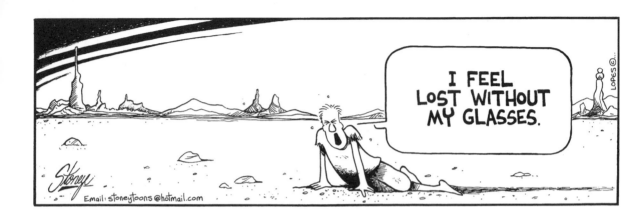

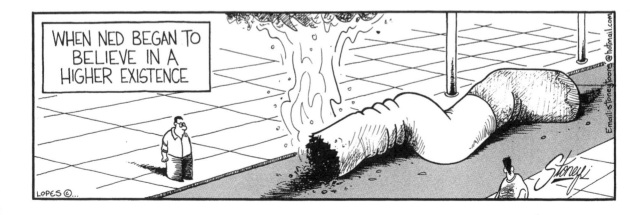

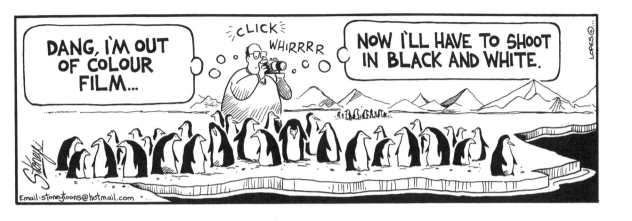
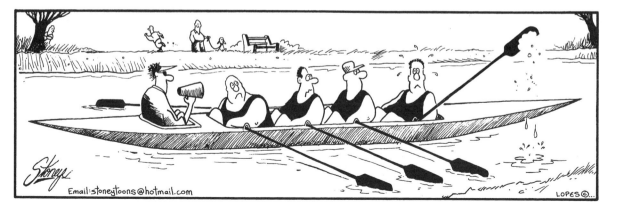

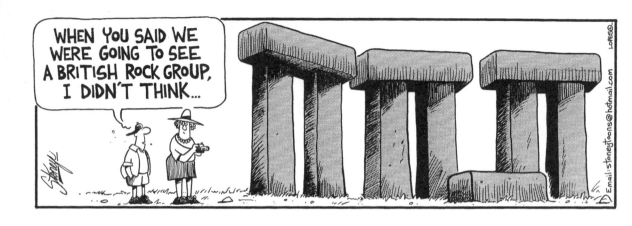
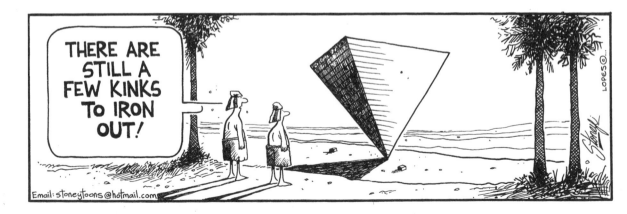